TO: CINDY

Because you warm my h...

♡ PATTY

A Girl and Her Heart

priceless love. timeless beauty.

Written by **Brooke Mardell** + Illustrated by **Jenny Lewis**

A Girl and Her Heart: priceless love. timeless beauty.
by Brooke Mardell
Illustrated by Jenny Lewis

307 E. Chapman Ave. Suite 204
Orange, CA. 92866

www.brookemardell.com

www.jennylewdesign.com

The text of this book is set in Minion Pro
The title text is set in Angeline Vintage and A Day Without Sun
The original illustrations for this book were created with graphite on Arches 140 lb. hot press paper, with added digital coloring rendered in Photoshop CC 2016
The watercolor effects used in the hearts were courtesy of freepik.com

First printing August 2016
ISBN 978-1-945228-00-1

Printed in California, United States of America

To Robyn

Once there was a girl.

And her heart.

Her heart was very special.
It was a gift from her Father.

"Oh, I love my heart!" said the girl.

The girl
took very
good care of her
heart. She read books about
how to tend her heart. How to protect
her heart. And how to make it shine.

The girl was very smart. One day her teacher said, "Here is a gold star."

And the girl put the shiny gold star on her heart. And it was cute. And she smiled.

The girl was also very kind. One day she helped an old man and he said, "Here is a purple ribbon."

And the girl tied the lovely purple ribbon next to the gold star on her heart. And it was sweet. And she smiled.

The girl was also very pretty. One day a little boy said shyly, "Here is a rose pin."

And the girl stuck the charming rose pin next to the purple ribbon next to the gold star on her heart. And it was crowded. But still, she smiled.

The girl was also very responsible. One day she worked hard to make sure all of her friends were happy. And they said, "Here is a silver medal."

And the girl put the sparkling silver medal next to the rose pin next to the purple ribbon next to the gold star on her heart.

And her heart grew heavy.

Still, the girl loved her heart.

She said, "It is time to protect my heart."

She found a box. And her heart fit inside the box. And she felt safe with her heart in the box.

But soon, the girl missed her heart. She would take it out of the box from time to time, and she would see the shiny gold star, the lovely purple ribbon, the charming rose pin, and the sparkling silver medal.

And the girl was sad. But she did not know why.

Each time the girl looked in the box, it grew harder and harder to see her heart. It was as though her heart had grown smaller inside the box.

Over time, the star faded, the ribbon frayed, the pin dulled, and the medal lost its luster.

The girl grew tired of looking, because she grew tired of being sad.

She went to her Father and told him,
"I miss my heart."
"Bring me the box," said her Father.

So the girl brought him the box.
But she could not open it.

"Help me!" cried the girl.
"Help me get to my heart!"

And her Father opened the box.
And the girl cried.

"WHERE IS MY HEART?!" she sobbed

"I will help you find it," said her Father.

And the girl was afraid. But she did not
know why.

First, the Father lifted the gold star. "Please don't take off my star," said the girl. "I am smart and this star makes my heart beautiful."

And her Father answered, "Gold stars matter not to me. What matters is your heart."

And the girl was confused.

Next, the Father untied the purple ribbon. "No, not that. I got it for being kind and it makes my heart lovely."

And her Father answered, "Ribbons do not decide whether a heart is lovely or kind."

And the girl was dismayed.

The Father then unclasped the rose pin
and it fell to the ground.

"Oh, my pin!" cried the girl, for with
each point He removed, she felt a little
pain. "You can't take that away from my
heart."

And her Father answered,
"I can take as well as give. You asked
me to help you find your heart.
This pin has pierced and torn it."

And the girl was angry.

Finally, the Father began to
lift the medal off her heart.

"NO!" shouted the girl.

She had never told her Father no before.
"I earned that and I will not let you have it!"

And her Father answered,
"I miss your heart as much as you do.
Will you trust me in this?"
And the girl said, "This hurts too
much." And her Father said, "I know."

"All I wanted was for you to help me
find my heart. But instead it is ruined.
Now it is ugly."

And her Father paused.
He looked down at her and said, "Do
you remember when I gave you your
heart?" "Yes," she answered. "It's one of
my favorite hearts," said the Father.

"Yes," she said, "that is why I cared for
it so. I made it beautiful by earning the
star, the ribbon, the pin and the medal."

"But you see," said the Father, "the
things that were meant to celebrate
your heart have now hidden it. Your
heart is most beautiful when it can be
fully seen."

And the girl was surprised.

"Who could love such a plain heart?"
she asked. "I will show you," He said.

And the Father took her hand,
while holding her heart,
and together they walked.

First the Father took her to see her teacher. "Hello, Teacher," said the girl, "you gave me my gold star because I was smart. But now my Father has taken it away and I think my heart is ugly without it."

But the teacher said, "I did not give you the gold star because you were smart, but because your heart was so radiant. I think your heart is beautiful without any of my silly gold stars."

And the girl smiled, shyly.

Next the Father took her to see the old
man. "Hello, Old Man," said the girl,
"you gave me my purple ribbon
because I was kind.
But now my Father has
taken it away and I
think my heart is
ugly without it."

But the old
man said, "I
did not give
you the purple
ribbon because
you were kind, but because your heart
was so lovely. I think your heart is
beautiful without my ribbon choking it."

And the girl smiled, hopefully.

So too the little boy told her, "I did not give you the pin because you were pretty, but because I liked being with you. I think your heart is beautiful without a rose."

And the girl smiled, genuinely.

Finally, her Father took her to see her friends. "Please, Friends, help me keep the medal you gave me. My Father has taken it away even though I earned it by taking care of you."

But her friends said, "We think the Father is right to take away our medal so you will know we love you more than we love what you do for us."

And the girl smiled, joyfully.

Looking at her heart, she asked her Father, "So it's not ruined? Even with these holes from the pin and marks left from the star?"

And the Father said "No, my girl,
your heart is not ruined. Your heart is
beautiful. These marks will always
be there to remind you of the lessons
you've learned, but they will no longer
hide your heart."

And the girl smiled, radiantly.

"Now I know my heart is beautiful
without anything I can add to it,"
said the girl.

"My heart is beautiful because it is mine,
and because I got it from you."

And the Father smiled.

CPSIA information can be obtained
at www.ICGtesting.com
Printed in the USA
LVOW06*1259131216
517067LV00007B/23/P